D1621647

STECK-VAUGHN FUNDAMENTAL SKILLS FOR WRITING: WORDS AND NUMBERS LITERACY

Printed in the U.S.A.

ISBN 978-0-544-79075-9

1 2 3 4 5 6 7 8 9 10 0918 24 23 22 21 20 19 18 17 16

4500577736   A B C D E F G

TABLE OF CONTENTS

LESSON 1: A, B, C

Aa   **Apple** begins with the letter <u>a</u>.

1. Write uppercase <u>A</u> and lowercase <u>a</u>.

A a   _____

2. Write the words that contain <u>A</u> and <u>a</u> on the lines provided.

cat	map	red	lost	Alice	ate
ran	sit	and	ax	tell	meal

_____ _____ _____ _____

_____ _____ _____ _____

Bb   **Ball** begins with the letter <u>b</u>.

3. Write uppercase <u>B</u> and lowercase <u>b</u>.

B b   _____

4. Write the words that contain <u>B</u> and <u>b</u> on the lines provided.

bad	big	sad	job	baby	lap
Ben	log	soap	bath	Bo	pet

_____ _____ _____ _____

_____ _____ _____

Cc   **Cup** begins with the letter <u>c</u>.

5. Write uppercase <u>C</u> and lowercase <u>c</u>.

C c   _____

6. Write the words that contain <u>C</u> and <u>c</u> on the lines provided.

corn	can	face	make	Carl	his
cat	pack	cry	dip	bet	sock

_____ _____ _____ _____

_____ _____ _____ _____

LESSON 2: *D, E, F*

Dd   ***Dog*** begins with the letter <u>d</u>.

1. Write uppercase <u>D</u> and lowercase <u>d</u>.

D d   _____

2. Write the words that contain <u>D</u> and <u>d</u> on the lines provided.

dad	good	bed	date	lip	cab
Dan	doll	bag	tap	sold	ride

_____   _____   _____   _____

_____   _____   _____   _____

Ee   ***Egg*** begins with the letter <u>e</u> .

3. Write uppercase <u>E</u> and lowercase <u>e</u>.

E e   _____

4. Write the words that contain <u>E</u> and <u>e</u> on the lines provided.

Ethan	bee	sit	elk	ship	pat
line	desk	lid	fire	ear	king

_____   _____   _____   _____

_____   _____   _____

Ff   ***Fox*** begins with the letter <u>f</u>.

5. Write uppercase <u>F</u> and lowercase <u>f</u>.

F f   _____

6. Write the words that contain <u>F</u> and <u>f</u> on the lines provided.

frog	Fred	gift	the	for	kite
golf	try	hen	lake	left	fix

_____   _____   _____   _____

_____   _____   _____

LESSON 3: *G, H, I*

Gg   ***Gift*** begins with the letter <u>g</u>.

1. Write uppercase <u>G</u> and lowercase <u>g</u>.

G g   _____

2. Write the words that contain <u>G</u> and <u>g</u> on the lines provided.

gate	log	pit	song	ghost	cold
flow	green	half	girl	rug	Gigi

_____   _____   _____   _____

_____   _____   _____   _____

Hh   ***Horse*** begins with the letter <u>h</u>.

3. Write uppercase <u>H</u> and lowercase <u>h</u>.

H h   _____

4. Write the words that contain <u>H</u> and <u>h</u> on the lines provided.

hill	fair	hot	ashes	hose	arch
check	hug	mild	Heidi	sofa	kick

_____   _____   _____   _____

_____   _____   _____   _____

Ii   ***Ink*** begins with the letter <u>i</u>.

5. Write uppercase <u>I</u> and lowercase <u>i</u>.

I i   _____

6. Write the words that contain <u>I</u> and <u>i</u> on the lines provided.

fly	is	dig	inch	buy	jar
iron	rice	Ingrid	jam	idea	Bill

_____   _____   _____   _____

_____   _____   _____   _____

LESSON 4: J, K, L

Jj   **Jeep** begins with the letter j.

1. Write uppercase J and lowercase j.

J j   _____

2. Write the words that contain J and j on the lines provided.

jog	pet	glad	jeans	June	jam
jump	just	juice	gem	lane	jingle

_____   _____   _____   _____

_____   _____   _____   _____

Kk   **Key** begins with the letter k .

3. Write uppercase K and lowercase k.

K k   _____

4. Write the words that contain K and k on the lines provided.

kick	bike	hip	kite	king	cup
rake	talk	come	cook	Kate	late

_____   _____   _____   _____

_____   _____   _____   _____

Ll   **Lion** begins with the letter l.

5. Write uppercase L and lowercase l.

L l   _____

6. Write the words that contain L and l on the lines provided.

lake	slow	pine	like	fast	know
leaf	tell	love	walk	send	Luke

_____   _____   _____   _____

_____   _____   _____   _____

LESSON 5: *M, N, O*

Mm **Money** begins with the letter <u>m</u>.

1. Write uppercase <u>M</u> and lowercase <u>m</u>.

M m _____

2. Write the words that contain <u>M</u> and <u>m</u> on the lines provided.

ham	mom	mat	nap	kind	tune
time	miss	came	wore	hen	Monique

_____ _____ _____ _____

_____ _____ _____

Nn **Nest** begins with the letter <u>n</u>.

3. Write uppercase <u>N</u> and lowercase <u>n</u>.

N n _____

4. Write the words that contain <u>N</u> and <u>n</u> on the lines provided.

fun	most	not	use	nine	Nala
rest	neck	knee	rain	seen	met

_____ _____ _____ _____

_____ _____ _____ _____

Oo **Ox** begins with the letter <u>o</u>.

5. Write uppercase <u>O</u> and lowercase <u>o</u>.

O o _____

6. Write the words that contain <u>O</u> and <u>o</u> on the lines provided.

Owen	off	cape	hope	win	ocean
math	pet	nose	boat	home	owl

_____ _____ _____ _____

_____ _____ _____ _____

LESSON 6: P, Q, R

Pp   **Piano** begins with the letter p̲.

1. Write uppercase P̲ and lowercase p̲.

    P p   _____

2. Write the words that contain P̲ and p̲ on the lines provided.

pop	shelf	Priya	nap	plant	west
pool	list	pie	grape	sea	tap

    _____   _____   _____   _____

    _____   _____   _____   _____

Qq   **Question** begins with the letter q̲ .

3. Write uppercase Q̲ and lowercase q̲.

    Q q   _____

4. Write the words that contain Q̲ and q̲ on the lines provided.

queen	size	quick	liquid	knit	Quincy
puppy	quilt	equal	quiet	quiz	cube

    _____   _____   _____   _____

    _____   _____   _____   _____

Rr   **Rake** begins with the letter r̲.

5. Write uppercase R̲ and lowercase r̲.

    R r   _____

6. Write the words that contain R̲ and r̲ on the lines provided.

run	team	where	purr	fast	road
store	side	Rory	room	may	turn

    _____   _____   _____   _____

    _____   _____   _____   _____

LESSON 7: S, T, U

Ss **Sun** begins with the letter s.

1. Write uppercase S and lowercase s.

   S s _____

2. Write the words that contain S and s on the lines provided.

sea	dress	wish	cent	sled	half
Sam	fence	seed	house	mix	hose

   _____ _____ _____ _____

   _____ _____ _____ _____

Tt **Tiger** begins with the letter t.

3. Write uppercase T and lowercase t.

   T t _____

4. Write the words that contain T and t on the lines provided.

tools	tent	tennis	map	lizard	Tess
goat	lime	rocket	star	cube	fan

   _____ _____ _____ _____

   _____ _____ _____

Uu **Umbrella** begins with the letter u.

5. Write uppercase U and lowercase u.

   U u _____

6. Write the words that contain U and u on the lines provided.

salt	up	baby	yarn	urn	unicycle
Uri	funny	tube	pony	fly	umpire

   _____ _____ _____ _____

   _____ _____ _____

LESSON 8: *V, W, X*

Vv   ***Vine*** begins with the letter <u>v</u>.

1. Write uppercase <u>V</u> and lowercase <u>v</u>.

V v   _____

2. Write the words that contain <u>V</u> and <u>v</u> on the lines provided.

van	love	Vince	cute	luck	vet
save	half	grave	mouse	cut	Dave

_____   _____   _____   _____

_____   _____   _____

Ww   ***Worm*** begins with the letter <u>w</u> .

3. Write uppercase <u>W</u> and lowercase <u>w</u>.

W w   _____

4. Write the words that contain <u>W</u> and <u>w</u> on the lines provided.

news	was	two	sweet	wise	music
Willa	under	many	crawl	busy	with

_____   _____   _____   _____

_____   _____   _____   _____

Xx   ***Ax*** contains the letter <u>x</u>.

5. Write uppercase <u>X</u> and lowercase <u>x</u>.

X x   _____

6. Write the words that contain <u>X</u> and <u>x</u> on the lines provided.

six	box	relax	fix	video	miss
wax	van	Xavier	taxes	fast	fox

_____   _____   _____   _____

_____   _____   _____   _____

LESSON 9: Y, Z

Yy   *Yo-yo* begins with the letter y.

1. Write uppercase Y and lowercase y.

Y y   _____

2. Write the words that contain Y and y on the lines provided.

Yamal	toys	you	yes	up	tie
dry	such	yellow	why	much	young

_____   _____   _____   _____

_____   _____   _____   _____

Zz   *Zebra* begins with the letter Z.

3. Write uppercase Z and lowercase z.

Z z   _____

4. Write the words that contain Z and z on the lines provided.

Zelda	maze	taste	zoo	buzz	prize
quiz	freeze	sing	close	dice	jazz

_____   _____   _____   _____

_____   _____   _____   _____

Draw a line for each uppercase letter to its lowercase letter.

1.	L	a
2.	P	f
3.	N	q
4.	A	g
5.	B	l
6.	Q	i
7.	G	p
8.	O	n
9.	F	o
10.	I	b

Which shows the correct pair of uppercase and lower case letters? Circle the choice that shows the correct partner letters.

11. R r   S c   T y   Q p

12. O c   I e   U u   V y

13. L k   F h   E e   A i

14. M n   J j   B d   G p

15. N v   W u   S z   M m

16. C k   X z   H l   B b

17. I i   E o   U v   Y i

18. C o   L l   D b   T f

19. K h   D d   Y j   P b

20. V u   Z s   P p   Q y

Circle the word that contains the uppercase or lowercase letter shown.

21. | f |

four   hat   lost   keep

22. | P |

quack   guess   Paul   Denver

23. | x |

cry   test   mist   oxen

24. | r |

spoon   frame   cat   bite

25. | y |

pants   gap   ice   yolk

26. | g |

name   Guam   get   pretty

27. | T |

tear   start   Texas   toe

28. | c |

cape   keep   old   rake

29. | o |

heart   shoe   tale   cup

30. | s |

Sally   fizz   hit   baseball

31. | k |

cobra   hall   until   walk

32. | N |

oven   noon   Nancy   Mike

33. | d |

bake   made   crab   hip

34. | l |

Lisa   have   long   kids

35. | m |

trim   waiter   dine   waves

LESSON 10: *B, C*

The letter <u>b</u> is a consonant.

Ball begins with the <u>b</u> sound.

Name each picture. Circle the pictures that begin with the <u>b</u> sound.

1.

Name each picture. If <u>b</u> stands for the missing letter, write <u>b</u> on the line provided.

2.

we___   ___rum   ca___in   ro___in

3.

mo___   win___ow   ___utter   ___ee

The letter <u>c</u> is a consonant.

Can begins with the <u>c</u> sound.

Name each picture. Circle the pictures that begin with the <u>c</u> sound.

4.

Name each picture. If <u>c</u> stands for the missing letter, write <u>c</u> on the line provided.

5.

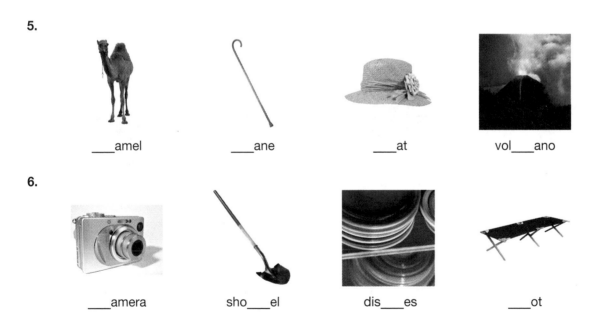

___amel   ___ane   ___at   vol___ano

6.

___amera   sho___el   dis___es   ___ot

LESSON 11: *D, F*

The letter <u>d</u> is a consonant.

Doll begins with the <u>d</u> sound.

Name each picture. Listen to the first sound. If the name begins with the <u>d</u> sound, write <u>d</u> on the line provided.

1.

   —   —   —   —

Name each picture. If <u>d</u> stands for the missing letter, write <u>d</u> on the line provided.

2.

  ___eer   ___ig   spi___er   shee___

3.

  han___   bi___e   can___y   wa___er

The letter f is a consonant.

Fish begins with the f sound.

Name each picture. Listen to the first sound. If the name begins with the f sound, write f on the line provided.

4.

_____   _____   _____   _____

Name each picture. If f stands for the missing letter, write f on the line provided.

5.

___ence   ___ox   ___irl   roo___

6.

boo___   el___   ru___er   ___an

LESSON 12: *G, H*

The letter g is a consonant.

Gum begins with the g sound.

Name each picture. Circle the pictures that begin with the g sound.

1.

Name each picture. If g stands for the missing letter, write g on the line provided.

2.

___olf   ___ame   wa___on   loc___

3.

pi___   ___ork   ro___e   bu___

The letter <u>h</u> is a consonant.

Hand begins with the <u>h</u> sound.

Name each picture. Circle the pictures that begin with the <u>h</u> sound.

4.

Name each picture. If <u>h</u> stands for the missing letter, write <u>h</u> on the line provided.

5.

   ___ce

___en

___ay

___ail

6.

   ___ook

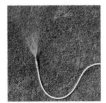   ___ose

   ___op

   ___eart

LESSON 13: *J, K*

The letter j is a consonant.

Jar begins with the j sound.

Name each picture. Listen to the first sound. If the name begins with the j sound, write j on the line provided.

1.

___   ___   ___   ___

Name each picture. If j stands for the missing letter, write j on the line provided.

2.

 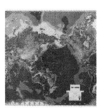 

___eep   ___ap   ___ack   ___ee

3.

___ump   ___ewelry   ___ope   ___ools

The letter <u>k</u> is a consonant.

King begins with the <u>k</u> sound.

Name each picture. Listen to the first sound. If the name begins with the <u>k</u> sound, write <u>k</u> on the line provided.

4.

———   ———   ———   ———

Name each picture. If <u>k</u> stands for the missing letter, write <u>k</u> on the line provided.

5.

___itten   ___oor   ___ick   tur___ey

6.

boo___   ru___   ___ape   skun___

LESSON 14: *L, M*

The letter <u>l</u> is a consonant.

Leaf begins with the <u>l</u> sound.

Name each picture. Circle the pictures that begin with the <u>l</u> sound.

1.

    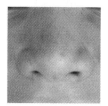

Name each picture. If <u>l</u> stands for the missing letter, write <u>l</u> on the line provided.

2.

   ___izard   came___   ow___   ___rame

3.

   ___ock   tea___   ___ire   ___ake

The letter <u>m</u> is a consonant.

Moon begins with the <u>m</u> sound.

Name each picture. Circle the pictures that begin with the <u>m</u> sound.

4.

Name each picture. If <u>m</u> stands for the missing letter, write <u>m</u> on the line provided.

5.

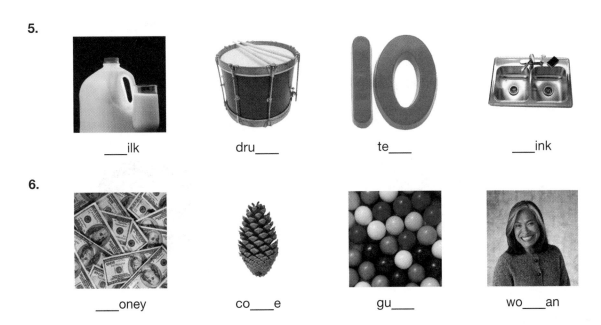

___ilk   dru___   te___   ___ink

6.

___oney   co___e   gu___   wo___an

LESSON 15: *N, P*

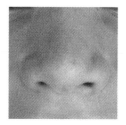

The letter <u>n</u> is a consonant.

Nose begins with the <u>n</u> sound.

Name each picture. Listen to the first sound. If the name begins with the <u>n</u> sound, write <u>n</u> on the line provided.

1.

___   ___   ___   ___

Name each picture. If <u>n</u> stands for the missing letter, write <u>n</u> on the line provided.

2.

___ickel   yar___   ___urse   su___

3.

___ail   wi___dow   ___et   ___eedle

The letter <u>p</u> is a consonant.

Pig begins with the <u>p</u> sound.

Name each picture. Listen to the first sound. If the name begins with the <u>p</u> sound, write <u>p</u> on the line provided.

4.

    ___   ___   ___   ___

Name each picture. If <u>p</u> stands for the missing letter, write <u>p</u> on the line provided.

5.

___ears   shi___   ro___in   ___ell

6.

___urse   foot___all   shee___   ___illow

LESSON 16: Q, R

The letter q is a consonant. Many q words start with qu.

Quail begins with the qu sound.

Name each picture. Circle the pictures that begin with the qu sound.

1.

Name each picture. If q stands for the missing letter, write q on the line provided.

2.

   ___uack   ___mbrella   e___ual   ___uilt

3.

 ___uarterback   ___uiet   ___ule   ___itty

The letter r is a consonant.

Rabbit begins with the r sound.

Name each picture. Circle the pictures that begin with the r sound.

4.

Name each picture. If r stands for the missing letter, write r on the line provided.

5.

___ocket   sta___s   ca___e   ___est

6.

___at   tu___tle   cu___e   ___ing

LESSON 17: *S, T*

The letter s is a consonant.

Seal begins with the s sound.

Name each picture. Listen to the first sound. If the name begins with the s sound, write s on the line provided.

1.

＿＿   ＿＿   ＿＿   ＿＿

Name each picture. If s stands for the missing letter, write s on the line provided.

2.

____oap   can___le   ____addle   new____paper

3.

____eaver   ro___e   ____ail   ____alad

The letter t is a consonant.

Tennis begins with the t sound.

Name each picture. Listen to the first sound. If the name begins with the t sound, write t on the line provided.

4.

___   ___   ___   ___

Name each picture. If t stands for the missing letter, write t on the line provided.

5.

___ent   elephan___   rea___   ___elevision

6.

___ime   mea___   ba___   ___ape

LESSON 18: V, W

The letter <u>v</u> is a consonant.

Van begins with the <u>v</u> sound.

Name each picture. Circle the pictures that begin with the <u>v</u> sound.

1.

Name each picture. If <u>v</u> stands for the missing letter, write <u>v</u> on the line provided.

2.

____ine   ____amp   ri____er   ____olleyball

3.

sho____el   ne____   ____ish   ____alentine

The letter <u>w</u> is a consonant.

Window begins with the <u>w</u> sound.

Name each picture. Circle the pictures that begin with the <u>w</u> sound.

4.

Name each picture. If <u>w</u> stands for the missing letter, write <u>w</u> on the line provided.

5.

| ___eak | sand___ich | lea___ | ___agon |

6.

| ___ell | ___ave | mi___er | ___atch |

LESSON 19: *X, Y, Z*

The letter <u>x</u> is a consonant.

Ox ends with the <u>x</u> sound.

Name each picture. Listen to the last sound. If the name ends with the <u>x</u> sound, write <u>x</u> on the line provided.

1.

   ___   ___   ___   ___

The letter <u>y</u> is a sometimes consonant. (The letter can also be a vowel, as in *money*.)

Yarn begins with the <u>y</u> sound.

Name each picture. If <u>y</u> stands for the missing letter, write <u>y</u> on the line provided.

2.

  ___o-yo   dri___er   ___ard   ___olcano

3.

  ___ell   ___awn   ___olk   ___uilt

The letter <u>z</u> is a consonant.

Zigzag begins with the <u>z</u> sound.

Name each picture. Listen to the first sound. If the name begins with the <u>z</u> sound, write <u>z</u> on the line provided.

4.

____   ____   ____   ____

Name each picture. If <u>z</u> stands for the missing letter, write <u>z</u> on the line provided.

5.

___oo   mo___   li___ard   time ___ones

6.

___ion   pri___e   ___ipper   roo___

LESSON 20: Consonant Blends: *S* Blends and *S* Blends with Three Letters

A **consonant blend** occurs when two or more consonants are together. The sounds blend together. Each sound is heard. You can hear a two-letter <u>s</u> blend at the beginning of these words:

<u>sk</u>ate   <u>sl</u>ide   <u>sm</u>ile   <u>sn</u>ail   <u>st</u>ar   <u>sc</u>ale

Name each picture. Listen to the first part of the word. Write the first two letters on the line provided.

| sp | sw | sk | sm | sc | st | sn | sl |

1. _____

2. _____

3. _____

4. _____

5. _____

6. _____

7. _____

8. _____

9. _____

10. _____

11. _____

12. _____

Some **consonant blends** have three letters. You can hear a three-letter s̲ blend at the beginning of these words:

<u>scr</u>eam   <u>spl</u>it   <u>spr</u>out   <u>str</u>eet

Name each picture. Listen to the first part of the word. Write the first three letters on the line provided.

scr	spl	spr	str

13.

_____

16.

_____

19.

_____

22.

_____

14.

_____

17.

_____

20.

_____

23.

_____

15.

_____

18.

_____

21.

_____

24.

_____

LESSON 21: Consonant Blends: *R* Blends, *L* Blends, and *TW* Blends

Remember that a consonant blend occurs when two or more consonants are together. You can hear a two-letter r blend at the beginning of these words:

bridge   crayon   dragon   frog   grill   prize   train

Name each picture. Listen to the first part of the word. Write the first two letters on the line provided.

br	pr	gr	cr	tr	fr	dr

1.

_____

4.

_____

7.

_____

10.

_____

2.

_____

5.

_____

8.

_____

11.

_____

3.

_____

6.

_____

9.

_____

12.

_____

You can hear a two-letter <u>l</u> blend at the beginning of these words:

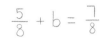

<u>bl</u>ock   <u>cl</u>ap   <u>fl</u>ag   <u>gl</u>ove   <u>pl</u>us

Name each picture. Listen to the first part of the word. Write the first two letters on the line provided.

bl	gl	cl	fl	pl

13.

_____

15.

_____

17.

_____

19.

_____

14.

_____

16.

_____

18.

_____

20.

_____

You can hear a <u>tw</u> blend at the beginning of the word *twelve*.

twelve

Name each picture. Circle the picture name.

21.

twenty
twirl
star

22.

twins
twigs
crowns

23.

twist
tweezers
flag

LESSON 22: Consonant Blends: Final Consonant Blends

A consonant blend can also occur at the end of a word. You can hear consonant blends at the ends of these words:

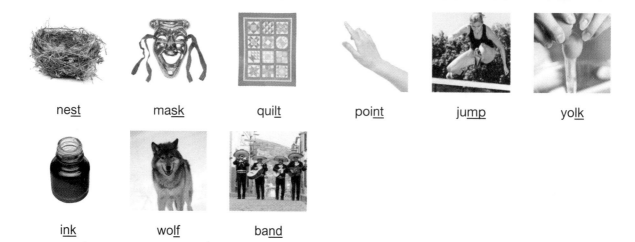

nest   mask   quilt   point   jump   yolk

ink   wolf   band

Name each picture. Listen to the last part of the word. Write the last two letters on the line provided.

| lk | sk | nt | nk | st | mp | lf |

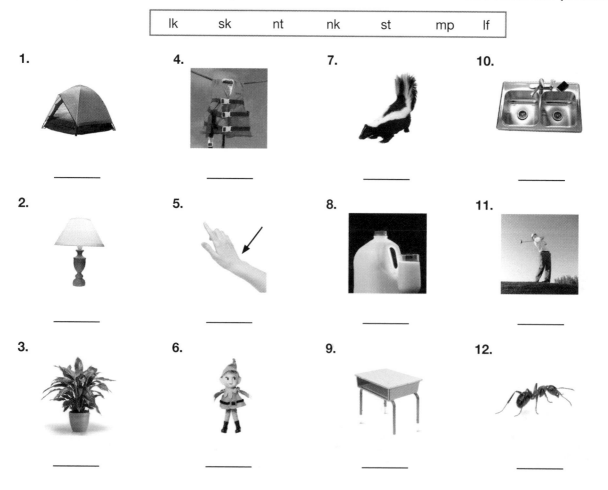

1. _____

2. _____

3. _____

4. _____

5. _____

6. _____

7. _____

8. _____

9. _____

10. _____

11. _____

12. _____

Name each picture. Circle the picture name.

13.

thump

toast

tent

14.

paint

plump

post

15.

just

jump

junk

16.

bump

bend

bark

17.

mask

mist

mold

18.

wand

wasp

wilt

19.

nest

neck

spin

20.

fist

friend

frost

21.

stand

silk

stump

22.

best

bank

band

23.

fork

fast

fold

24.

bank

belt

band

Name each picture. Circle the letter that stands for the <u>beginning</u> sound.

1.

s f r

5.

l p b

9.

v b n

13.

s w d

2.

d k x

6.

n w k

10.

g h k

14.

r f t

3.

m l j

7.

n p v

11.

l r k

15.

b k d

4.

s n t

8.

r w k

12.

m d b

16.

g k r

Name each picture. Circle the letter that stands for the <u>ending</u> sound.

17.

b   p   t

18.

h   g   s

19.

k   d   y

20.

l   n   p

21.

d   x   v

22.

g   h   k

23.

l   f   w

24.

t   h   z

25.

h   k   d

26.

r   s   m

27.

d   t   b

28.

p   s   l

29.

g   p   r

30.

d   g   r

31.

p   r   l

32.

k   s   r

Name each picture. Select the blend that completes each word and write it on the line provided.

33.

fr
fl
tr
sl

____uit

37.

cl
bl
fl
sl

____ock

41.

spl
squ
str
scr

____eam

34.

sk
nt
sh
mp

ju____

38.

rt
st
sk
tw

____elve

42.

sk
st
fl
sl

____ed

35.

st
rt
mp
sk

che____

39.

cl
dr
st
cr

____um

43.

nt
mp
sp
nd

ha____

36.

sc
sm
sn
tw

____ail

40.

br
fl
cr
sk

____own

44.

nd
nt
mp
sk

sta____

LESSON 23: Short *a*

Apple begins with the <u>short a</u> vowel sound. You can also hear the <u>short a</u> sound in the middle of words. The word ***hat*** has a <u>short a</u> sound in the middle.

Name each picture. Circle the pictures that contain the <u>short a</u> sound.

1.

2.

3.

4.

LESSON 24: Long *a*

Rake has the <u>long a</u> vowel sound. Adding silent *e* to the end of a word can make the vowel sound long. The letters ***ai***, as in ***sail***, and ***ay***, as in ***day***, can also stand for the <u>long a</u> vowel sound.

Name each picture. Circle the pictures that contain the <u>long a</u> sound.

1.

2.

3.

4.

Fundamental Skills for Writing

LESSON 25: Short *e*

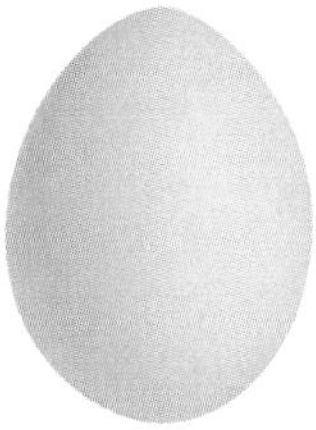

Egg begins with the short e vowel sound. You can also hear the short e sound in the middle of words. The word ***check*** has a short e sound in the middle.

Name each picture. Circle the pictures that contain the short e sound.

1.

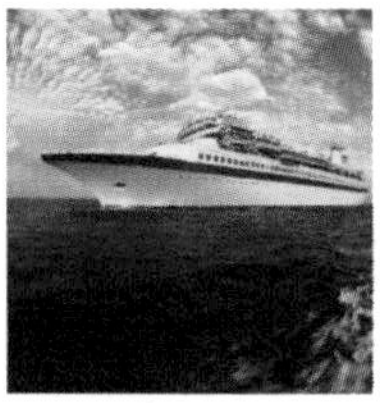  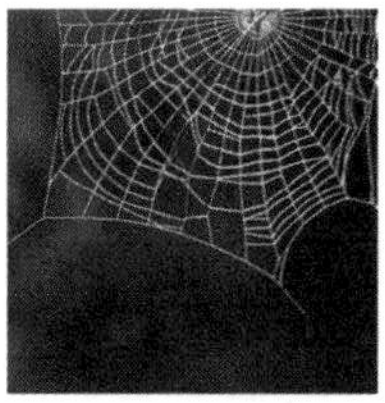 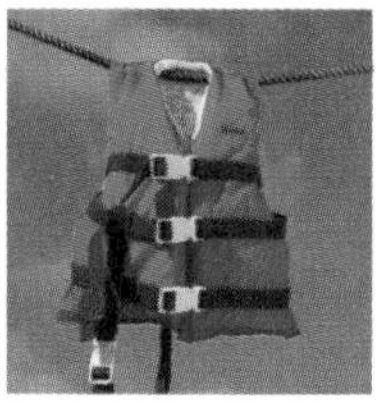

2.

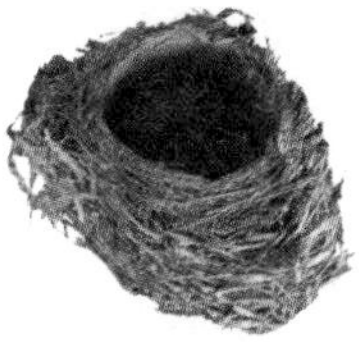 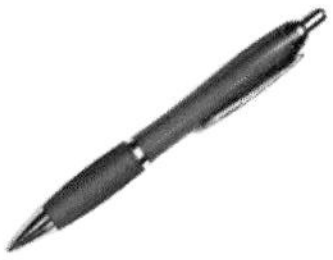 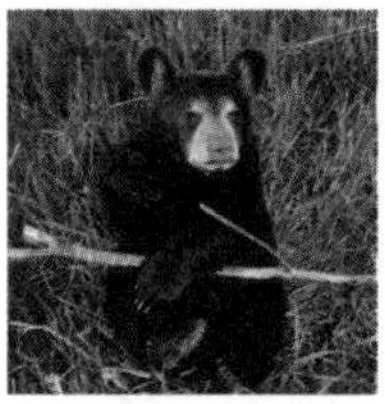 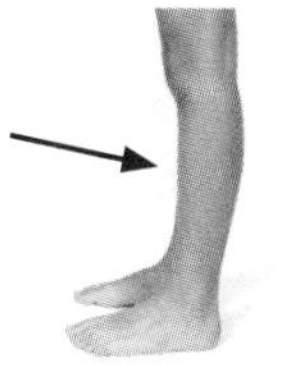

3.

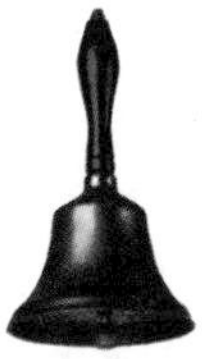 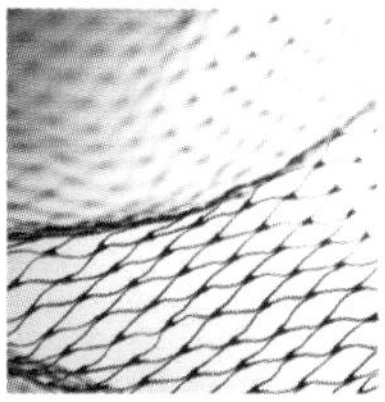 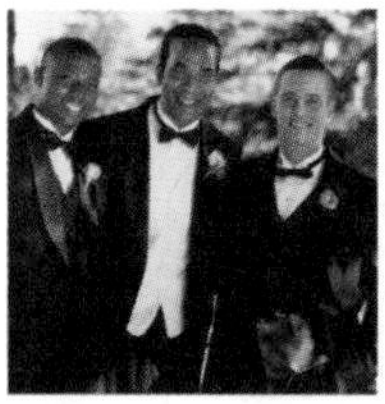 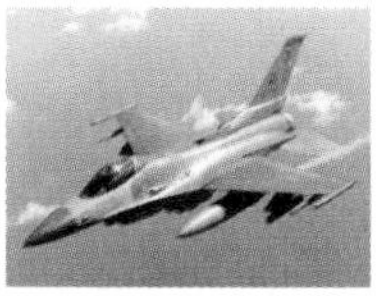

4.

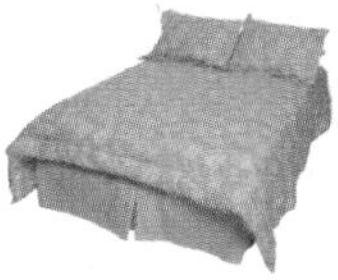 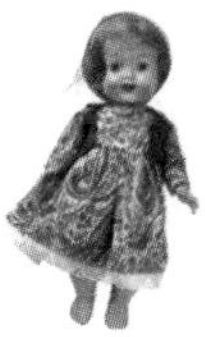 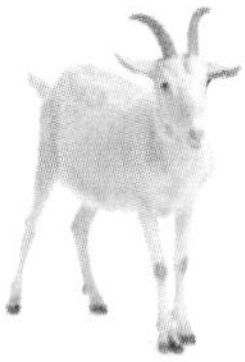 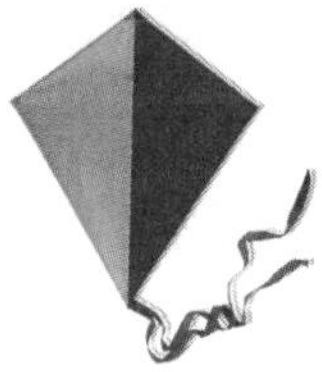

LESSON 26: Long *e*

Jeep has the <u>long e</u> vowel sound. The letters ***ee*** can stand for the <u>long e</u> vowel sound. The letters ***ea***, as in ***peas***, can also stand for the <u>long e</u> vowel sound.

Name each picture. Circle the pictures that contain the <u>long e</u> sound.

1.

2.

3.

4.

LESSON 27: Short *i*

Ink begins with the <u>short i</u> vowel sound. You can also hear the <u>short i</u> sound in the middle of words. The word ***lip*** has a <u>short i</u> sound in the middle.

Name each picture. Circle the pictures that contain the <u>short i</u> sound.

1.

2.

3.

  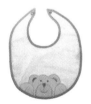 

4.

LESSON 28: Long *i*

Lime has the <u>long i</u> vowel sound. Adding silent *e* to the end of a word can make the vowel sound long.

Name each picture. Circle the pictures that contain the <u>long i</u> sound.

1.

2.

3.

4.

LESSON 29: Short *o*

Ox begins with the <u>short o</u> vowel sound. You can also hear the <u>short o</u> sound in the middle of words. The word ***spot*** has a <u>short o</u> sound in the middle.

Name each picture. Circle the pictures that contain the <u>short o</u> sound.

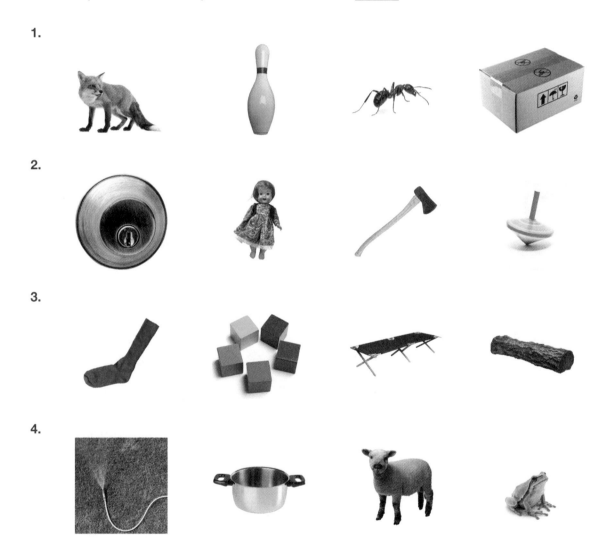

1.

2.

3.

4.

LESSON 30: Long *o*

Rope has the <u>long o</u> vowel sound. Adding silent *e* to the end of a word can make the vowel sound long. The letters ***oa***, as in ***coat***, can also stand for the <u>long o</u> vowel sound.

Name each picture. Circle the pictures that contain the <u>long o</u> sound.

1.
 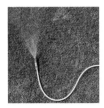 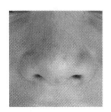 

2.

3.

4.

LESSON 31: Short *u*

Up begins with the <u>short u</u> vowel sound. You can also hear the <u>short u</u> sound in the middle of words. The word ***plum*** has a <u>short u</u> sound in the middle.

Name each picture. Circle the pictures that contain the <u>short u</u> sound.

1.

2.

3.

4.

LESSON 32: Long *u*

Fuse has the <u>long u</u> vowel sound. Adding silent *e* to the end of a word can make the vowel sound long.

Name each picture. Circle the pictures that contain the <u>long u</u> sound.

1.

2.

3.

4.

LESSON 33: Vowel Pairs: *EA, EI*

A **vowel pair** can have a short vowel sound, a long vowel sound, or a sound all its own.

The vowel pair <u>ea</u> can stand for the <u>short e</u> sound you hear in **bread**.
The vowel pair <u>ei</u> can stand for the <u>long a</u> sound you hear in **weigh**.

bread

weigh

Name each picture. Write <u>ea</u> or <u>ei</u> on the line to complete the word.

1.

r___n

5.

p___r

9.

f___ther

13.

sl___gh

2.

h___d

6.

w___ght

10.

___ght

14.

tr___sure

3.

v___l

7.

tr___d

11.

thr___d

15.

v___ns

4.

sw___ter

8.

n___ghbors

12.

spr___d

16.

w___ther

LESSON 34: Vowel Pairs: OO

The vowel pair <u>oo</u> can stand for the vowel sounds you hear in **book** and **moon**.

b<u>oo</u>k   m<u>oo</u>n

Write the word that names each picture on the line provided.

1.

would
wood
word

_____

5.

racing
racket
raccoon

_____

9.

kangaroo
kettle
kitchen

_____

2.

roof
ruff
root

_____

6.

school
scold
should

_____

10.

ballet
baboon
balloon

_____

3.

hoop
honk
hook

_____

7.

zigzag
zebra
zoo

_____

11.

book
bore
boot

_____

4.

wool
work
wall

_____

8.

pool
pour
pop

_____

12.

sport
spot
spoon

_____

LESSON 35: Vowel Pairs: *EW, UI*

The vowel pairs <u>ew</u> and <u>ui</u> can stand for the vowel sound you hear in **screw** and **fruit**.

screw

fr<u>ui</u>t

Write the word that names each picture on the line provided.

1.

jester

jewel

jelly

_____

3.

needle

newspaper

noontime

_____

5.

chew

choose

cherry

_____

2.

suit

soup

soon

_____

4.

stem

straw

stew

_____

6.

junk

judge

juice

_____

Choose the word in the box that completes each sentence. Write the word on the line provided.

| blew | bruise | cruise | drew | few | flew | fruit | juicy | new | uniform |

7. The Chen family went on a _____ to the South Pacific.

8. They sailed on a freshly painted, _____ ship.

9. Sam Chen could tell who the captain was by his _____.

10. The Chens visited quite a _____ beautiful islands.

11. A soft, warm breeze _____ through the palm trees.

12. Colorful birds _____ all around and perched nearby.

13. Sam _____ the birds in his travel journal.

14. Sam ate the mango but would not eat the banana with the _____.

15. Mrs. Chen fed the birds little pieces of _____.

16. The birds loved the _____ fruit!

LESSON 36: Vowel Pairs: *AU, AW, AL*

The vowel pairs <u>au</u> and <u>aw</u> can stand for the vowel sound you hear in **haul** and **paw**.
The letters <u>al</u> can stand for the vowel sound you hear in **chalk** and **ball**.

h<u>au</u>l

p<u>aw</u>

ch<u>al</u>k

b<u>al</u>l

Name each picture. Write <u>au</u>, <u>aw</u>, or <u>al</u> on the line to complete the word.

1.

f___l

5.

s___

9.

s___cer

13.

d___n

2.

y___n

6.

f___cet

10.

cr___l

14.

sh___l

3.

w___k

7.

l___n

11.

astron___t

15.

s___t

4.

v___lt

8.

w___l

12.

h___k

16.

___tumn

LESSON 37: Vowel Pairs: *OU*

The vowel pair <u>ou</u> can stand for the vowel sound you hear in **mouse**.

m<u>ou</u>se

Name each picture. If the word has the same vowel sound that you hear in *mouse*, write the vowel pair <u>ou</u> on the line to complete the word.

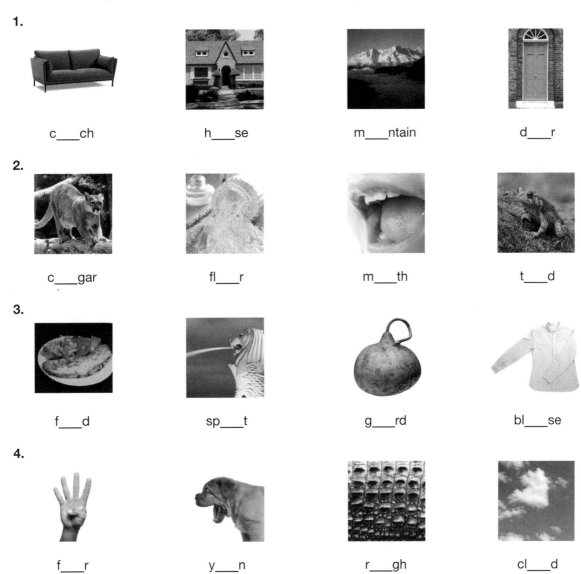

1.

c____ch   h____se   m____ntain   d____r

2.

c____gar   fl____r   m____th   t____d

3.

f____d   sp____t   g____rd   bl____se

4.

f____r   y____n   r____gh   cl____d

LESSON 38: Vowel Pairs: *OW, OY, OI*

The vowel pair <u>ow</u> can stand for the sound you hear in **cow**. It can also stand for the <u>long o</u> sound you hear in **crow**.

The vowel pairs <u>oy</u> and <u>oi</u> can stand for the sound you hear in **boy** and **oil**.

c<u>ow</u>

cr<u>ow</u>

b<u>oy</u>

<u>oi</u>l

The words at the left name the pictures in each row. Write each word under its picture.

toys soil point	**1.** _____	**2.** _____	**3.** _____
coil broil noise	**4.** _____	**5.** _____	**6.** _____
boil oyster foil	**7.** _____	**8.** _____	**9.** _____
crown snow flower	**10.** _____	**11.** _____	**12.** _____
clown owl coins	**13.** _____	**14.** _____	**15.** _____

LESSON 39: *R*-controlled Vowels

When r follows a vowel, it changes the vowel sound. The vowel is neither long nor short.
You can hear the ar sound in **car**, and you can hear the or sound in **corn**.
The letter pairs ur, ir, and er all have the same sound. You can hear this sound in **church**, **bird**, and **herd**.

car

corn

church

bird

herd

Name each picture. Circle the pictures that have the ar sound.

1.

Name each picture. Circle the pictures that have the or sound.

2.

Find the word in the box that names each picture. Write the word on the line provided.

| nurse | fern | girl | purse | surf | hammer | stir | skirt |

3.

_____

5.

_____

7.

_____

9.

_____

4.

_____

6.

_____

8.

_____

10.

_____

Say the name of each picture. What <u>short vowel</u> sound do you hear—short *a, e, i, o,* or *u*? Write the vowel on the first line. Then write the word on the second line.

| bed | hat | gum | vest | fish | mop | pig | bib | cat | lamp | lock | sun |

1.

short ____,

word: _____

7.

short ____,

word: _____

2.

short ____,

word: _____

8.

short ____,

word: _____

3.

short ____,

word: _____

9.

short ____,

word: _____

4.

short ____,

word: _____

10.

short ____,

word: _____

5.

short ____,

word: _____

11.

short ____,

word: _____

6.

short ____,

word: _____

12.

short ____,

word: _____

Say the name of each picture. What <u>long vowel</u> sound do you hear—long *a, e, i, o,* or *u*? Write the vowel on the first line. Then write the word on the second line.

| leaf | play | kite | eagle | cane | hose | bone | mule | sail | hay | toad | feet |

13.

long ____,

word: _____

19.

long ____,

word: _____

14.

long ____,

word: _____

20.

long ____,

word: _____

15.

long ____,

word: _____

21.

long ____,

word: _____

16.

long ____,

word: _____

22.

long ____,

word: _____

17.

long ____,

word: _____

23.

long ____,

word: _____

18.

long ____,

word: _____

24.

long ____,

word: _____

Select the word that names each picture and write it on the line provided.

25.

walk
what
wall

_____

28.

surf
skirt

_____

31.

burn
barn

_____

26.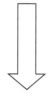

door
dock
down

_____

29.

fork
first

_____

32.

car
cord

_____

27.

suit
sew
soon

_____

30.

germ
girl

_____

33.

form
fern

_____

Name each picture. Select the letter or letters that complete the word and write them on the lines provided.

34.

i
o
u
a

b___x

37.

ur
er
ar
ir

sh___k

40.

er
or
ur
ir

st___k

43.

o
u
e
a

d___ck

35.

i
a
u
e

b___ke

38.

al
au
aw
ea

cr___l

41.

i
e
u
o

r___pe

44.

ou
oy
ay
al

b___

36.

aw
ow
oo
ui

j___ce

39.

oo
ai
ou
oa

g___t

42.

a
u
o
i

c___ke

45.

ar
or
ir
ur

st___

LESSON 40: Word Patterns *ad, and, ast, at*

Word families are groups of words that have a common pattern. Words in the same word family share similar letters and have similar sounds.

Examples:

Dad and *sad* are words in the <u>ad</u> word family.
They both have the letters <u>ad</u> and the "ad" sound.

dad   sad

Band and *hand* are words in the <u>and</u> word family.
They both have the letters <u>and</u> and the "and" sound.

band   hand

Fast and *mast* are words in the <u>ast</u> word family.
They both have the letters <u>ast</u> and the "ast" sound.

fast   mast

Cat and *rat* are words in the <u>at</u> word family.
They both have the letters <u>at</u> and the "at" sound.

cat   rat

PRACTICE

1. Write the words that are part of the <u>ad</u> word family on the lines provided.

| glad | rail | map | had | cash | clad | fall | jar | rake | brad |

_____ _____ _____ _____

2. Write the words that are part of the <u>and</u> word family on the lines provided.

| stand | make | snack | bland | grand | cat | tail | brand | than | snap |

_____ _____ _____ _____

3. Write the words that are part of the <u>ast</u> word family on the lines provided.

| trash | vast | fake | mast | sack | blast | mat | bad | past | gate |

_____ _____ _____ _____

4. Write the words that are part of the <u>at</u> word family on the lines provided.

chat	bank	splat	clap	that	slat	gnat	cage	fat	back

_____ _____ _____ _____ _____ _____

Name each picture. Draw a line to match the pictures that belong to the same word family.

mad	cast	pad	hat	land	last	sand	mat

5.

6.

7.

8.

Write a sentence with at least two words from the same word family. Underline the words in the sentence.

9. <u>ad</u> word family:

_____

_____

10. <u>and</u> word family:

_____

_____

11. <u>ast</u> word family:

_____

_____

12. <u>at</u> word family:

_____

_____

LESSON 41: Word Patterns *et, en, ent, end*

Here are words that are part of the <u>et</u>, <u>en</u>, <u>ent</u>, and <u>end</u> word families.

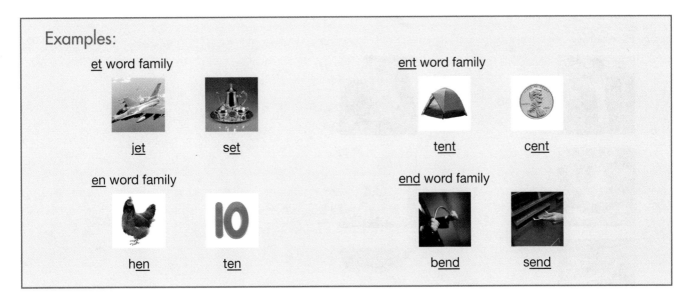

Examples:

<u>et</u> word family

jet   set

<u>en</u> word family

hen   ten

<u>ent</u> word family

tent   cent

<u>end</u> word family

bend   send

PRACTICE

1. Write the words that are part of the <u>et</u> word family on the lines provided.

| rest | met | spell | get | wet | bet | yet | test | let | nest |

_____ _____ _____ _____ _____ _____

2. Write the words that are part of the <u>en</u> word family on the lines provided.

| den | sell | test | when | oven | let | then | heel | children | pen |

_____ _____ _____ _____ _____ _____

3. Write the words that are part of the <u>ent</u> word family on the lines provided.

| lent | rent | men | spent | tell | best | event | feel | bent | went |

_____ _____ _____ _____ _____ _____

4. Write the words that are part of the <u>end</u> word family on the lines provided.

| lend | accent | cell | mend | depend | trend | spend | often | peel | attend |

_____ _____ _____ _____ _____ _____

Name each picture. Draw a line to match the pictures that belong to the same word family.

spend	pen	net	vent	men	vet	blend	dent

5.

6.

7.

8.

Write a sentence with at least two words from the same word family. Underline the words in the sentence.

9. et word family:

_____

_____

10. en word family:

_____

_____

11. ent word family:

_____

_____

12. end word family:

_____

_____

LESSON 42: Word Patterns *ig, in, ink, ist*

Here are words that are part of the <u>ig</u>, <u>in</u>, <u>ink</u>, and <u>ist</u> word families.

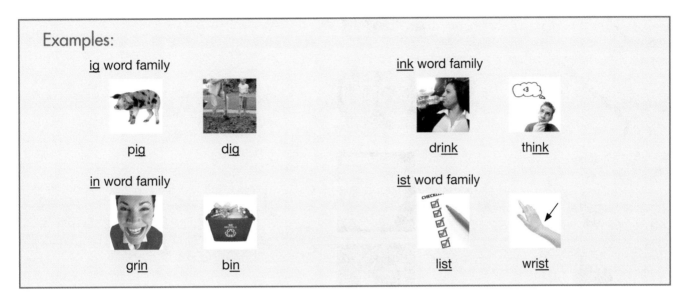

Examples:

ig word family

pig   dig

in word family

grin   bin

ink word family

drink   think

ist word family

list   wrist

PRACTICE

1. Write the words that are part of the <u>ig</u> word family on the lines provided.

| jig | kit | fig | tide | zig | sprig | ice | gig | chill | rig |

_____   _____   _____   _____   _____   _____

2. Write the words that are part of the <u>in</u> word family on the lines provided.

| chin | sing | fin | tight | shin | skin | thin | tick | win | hide |

_____   _____   _____   _____   _____   _____

3. Write the words that are part of the <u>ink</u> word family on the lines provided.

| rip | blink | vine | wink | rink | pink | sick | stink | life | shrink |

_____   _____   _____   _____   _____   _____

4. Write the words that are part of the <u>ist</u> word family on the lines provided.

| mist | price | quick | side | gist | wife | mile | tide | wing | exist |

_____   _____   _____

Name each picture. Draw a line to match the pictures that belong to the same word family.

| twins | ink | fist | wig | sink | pin | twig | twist |

5.

6.

7.

8.

Write a sentence with at least two words from the same word family. Underline the words in the sentence.

9. ig word family:

_____

_____

10. in word family:

_____

_____

11. ink word family:

_____

_____

12. ist word family:

_____

_____

LESSON 43: Word Patterns *ot, op, ong*

Here are words that are part of the <u>ot</u>, <u>op</u>, and <u>ong</u> word families.

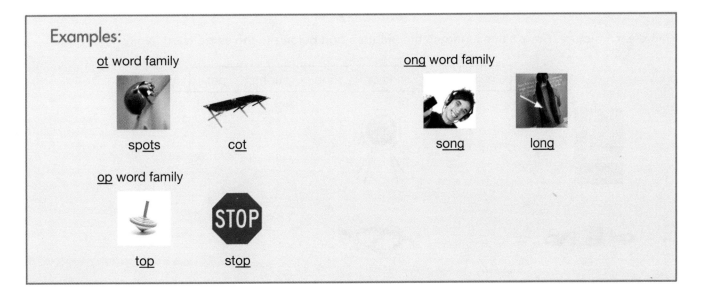

Examples:

<u>ot</u> word family

sp<u>ots</u>　　　c<u>ot</u>

<u>ong</u> word family

s<u>ong</u>　　　l<u>ong</u>

<u>op</u> word family

t<u>op</u>　　　st<u>op</u>

PRACTICE

1. Write the words that are part of the <u>ot</u> word family on the lines provided.

not	trot	rot	core	shout	got	plot	took	clot	dock

_____ _____ _____ _____ _____ _____

2. Write the words that are part of the <u>op</u> word family on the lines provided.

flop	sop	fool	plop	horn	pout	chop	boil	drop	bop

_____ _____ _____ _____ _____ _____

3. Write the words that are part of the <u>ong</u> word family on the lines provided.

soil	strong	bore	along	mouse	roof	birdsong	torn	about	wrong

_____ _____ _____ _____

Draw a line connecting the two words that are in the same word family.

4. forgot   prop

5. prong   lot

6. shop   belong

Name each picture. Draw a line to match the pictures that belong to the same word family.

hop	gong	knot	mop	strong	pot

7.

8.

9.

Write a sentence with at least two words from the same word family. Underline the words in the sentence.

10. ot word family:

_____

_____

11. op word family:

_____

_____

12. ong word family:

_____

_____

LESSON 44: Word Patterns *ug, un, ust, ump*

Here are words that are part of the ug, un, ust, and ump word families.

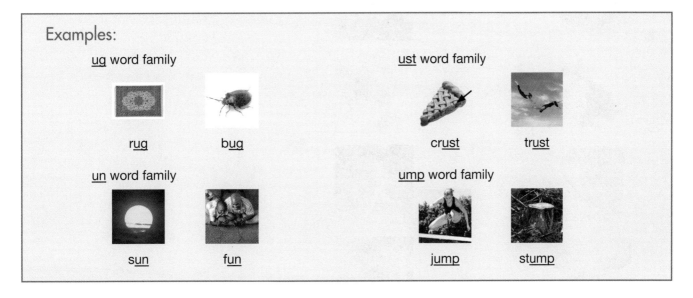

Examples:

ug word family

rug   bug

un word family

sun   fun

ust word family

crust   trust

ump word family

jump   stump

PRACTICE

1. Write the words that are part of the ug word family on the lines provided.

tug	jug	luck	lug	sunk	hug	smug	junk	dug	bus

_____ _____ _____ _____ _____ _____

2. Write the words that are part of the un word family on the lines provided.

tusk	bump	trunk	stun	nun	pun	shun	cut	spun	gun

_____ _____ _____ _____ _____ _____

3. Write the words that are part of the ust word family on the lines provided.

snug	tuck	just	must	gust	adjust	skunk	tune	cut	dusk

_____ _____ _____ _____

4. Write the words that are part of the ump word family on the lines provided.

duck	trump	lump	flunk	slump	dump	snug	plump	gut	thump

_____ _____ _____ _____ _____

Name each picture. Draw a line to match the pictures that belong to the same word family.

| crust | bump | bun | plug | dust | mug | pump | run |

5.

6.

7.

8.

Write a sentence with at least two words from the same word family. Underline the words in the sentence.

9. ug word family:

_____

_____

10. un word family:

_____

_____

11. ust word family:

_____

_____

12. ump word family:

_____

_____

LESSON 45: Writing Sight Words *a, and, the, you, have*

Sight words are words that appear often in reading materials. Because many sight words cannot be "sounded out," readers must learn them by sight.

a	<u>A</u> man rode the bus.	Jen gave Mike <u>a</u> book.
and	Bo <u>and</u> Jim are grilling.	You should not drive <u>and</u> text.
the	<u>The</u> music is loud.	Emma is walking to <u>the</u> store.
you	Missy gave <u>you</u> the bag.	<u>You</u> will like the cake.
have	We <u>have</u> a meeting today.	<u>Have</u> you seen my keys?

PRACTICE

Choose the word from the box that correctly completes the sentence. Write the word on the line.

a	and	the	you	have

1. Will Sam give you _____ ride home?

2. Nina _____ Nell are sisters.

3. Have you read _____ new rules?

4. James will meet _____.

5. We _____ a great idea.

6. Are _____ kids playing outside?

7. She will get more paper _____ pens.

8. Nurses _____ a difficult job.

9. We saw _____ rainbow after the storm.

10. Do _____ know who is sick?

Write a sentence using the word shown. Underline the word in the sentence.

11. a: _____

12. and: _____

13. the: _____

14. you: _____

15. have: _____

LESSON 46: Writing Sight Words *one, word, can, said, little*

Reading and writing **sight words** over and over is the best way to learn them.

one	Bill has <u>one</u> brother.	<u>One</u> tire on the car is flat.
word	What is the meaning of that <u>word</u>?	He has the final <u>word</u>.
can	I <u>can</u> take the kids to school.	<u>Can</u> you wait for me?
said	Tony <u>said</u> he'd be late.	"I'll go with you," she <u>said</u>.
little	The <u>little</u> girl hugged her doll.	I have only a <u>little</u> money.

PRACTICE

Choose the word from the box that correctly completes the sentence. Write the word on the line.

one	word	can	said	little

1. Please take _____ ticket.

2. Where _____ I put my things?

3. We don't know what this _____ means.

4. We have a _____ time before the bus arrives.

5. He _____ he needs two more nails.

6. I have _____ dog and two cats.

7. _____ she speak Spanish?

8. Please spell the _____ for me.

9. I didn't hear what he _____.

10. Maya played softball when she was _____.

Write a sentence using the word shown. Underline the word in the sentence.

11. one: _____

12. word: _____

13. can:_____

14. said: _____

15. little: _____

LESSON 47: Recognizing Homonyms *eye, I; ate, eight*

Homonyms are words that sound alike but have different meanings.

Examples:

A tear fell from his **eye**.   *Eye* refers to a sight organ and an ability to watch.
I don't like to see you cry.   *I* is a letter and a pronoun referring to yourself.

She **ate** two slices of pizza.   *Ate* is the past tense verb form of *eat*.
Eight slices are left.   *Eight* is the word form of the number 8.

PRACTICE

On the line provided, write the word that best completes the sentence.

1. I   Eye   _____ am going to ride my bike to work.

2. ate   eight   She has _____ books to return to the library.

3. I   eye   Raj, Jack, and _____ are at the pool.

4. ate   eight   The horse _____ the carrot.

5. I   eye   My left _____ is swollen.

6. ate   eight   He _____ all the ice cream.

7. I   eye   Dean will keep an _____ on the baby.

8. ate   eight   Allie _____ dinner at Mindy's house.

9. I   Eye   _____ haven't seen that movie.

10. Ate   Eight   _____ people are needed for the night shift.

Write a sentence using the word shown. Underline the word in the sentence.

11. eye: _____

12. I: _____

13. ate: _____

14. eight: _____

LESSON 48: Recognizing Homonyms *whole, hole; see, sea*

Words that sound alike but have different meanings are called **homonyms**.

Examples:

Get the **whole** box of sweaters.   *Whole* refers to an entire thing.
This sweater has a **hole** in it.   *Hole* refers to an opening.

The **sea** is calm today.   *Sea* refers to an ocean or a large body of water.
I can **see** dolphins in the cove.   *See* refers to the ability of sight or to be aware.

PRACTICE

On the line provided, write the word that best completes the sentence.

1. whole   hole   She wanted to hear the _____ story.

2. see   sea   Did you _____ the new schedule?

3. whole   hole   The dog's _____ body was muddy.

4. see   sea   The doctor will _____ you now.

5. whole   hole   We need to dig a large _____ to plant the tree.

6. see   sea   Large fish can be found in the _____.

7. whole   hole   Have you known her your _____ life?

8. see   sea   The _____ was choppy during the storm.

9. whole   hole   The water drains through a _____ in the floor.

10. see   sea   Let's _____ how the interview goes.

Write a sentence using the word shown. Underline the word in the sentence.

11. whole: _____

12. hole: _____

13. see: _____

14. sea: _____

LESSON 49: Using the Suffixes -s, -ed

Words can have different parts. The main part of a word is known as the **base**. An ending part is called a **suffix**. The ending -s and -ed are two common suffixes.

The suffix -s can make a base word plural, or more than one.

Example:

The <u>flower</u> is yellow.   The <u>flowers</u> are pretty.

The suffix -ed can make a base word show a past action.

Example:

I <u>plant</u> a garden every year.   I <u>planted</u> my garden last week.

PRACTICE

Add -s to the word and write the new word on the line provided. Then write a sentence with the new word.

1. <u>light</u> becomes _____

   _____

2. <u>pen</u> becomes _____

   _____

3. <u>door</u> becomes _____

   _____

4. <u>cup</u> becomes _____

   _____

5. <u>room</u> becomes _____

   _____

Add -ed to the word and write the new word on the line provided. Then write a sentence with the new word.

6. <u>turn</u> becomes _____

   _____

7. <u>spill</u> becomes _____

   _____

8. <u>lock</u> becomes _____

   _____

9. <u>help</u> becomes _____

   _____

10. <u>hand</u> becomes _____

   _____

LESSON 50: Using the Suffix -ing

The suffix -ing is another common suffix that can be added to base words to make new words.

Sometimes, an -ing word is a verb. A verb is a word that shows action or a state of being. Other times, an -ing word is a gerund. A gerund is a noun made from a verb by adding -ing.

Example:

read + -ing = reading

Dana is reading to her son. (verb)

Reading is one of her favorite activities. (gerund)

PRACTICE

Add -ing to the word to create a new word. Write the new word on the line provided.

1. talk + -ing = _____

2. pull + -ing = _____

3. do + -ing = _____

4. sort + -ing = _____

5. walk + -ing = _____

6. push + -ing = _____

7. look + -ing = _____

8. go + -ing = _____

9. jump + -ing = _____

10. sing + -ing = _____

Add -ing to the word and write the new word on the line provided. Then write a sentence with the new word. You can use the new word as a verb or as a gerund.

11. eat becomes _____

_____

12. wish becomes _____

_____

13. think becomes _____

_____

14. drink becomes _____

_____

15. pay becomes _____

_____

16. visit becomes _____

_____

17. cook becomes _____

_____

18. climb becomes _____

_____

For each item, write the words from the box that are in the same word family.

rug	rat	sun	past	must	hand	jump	sad	not	spend
stop	went	long	then	dig	met	bin	list	think	win
mist	twig	jet	wrong	ten	chop	rent	plot	lend	stump
glad	rust	sand	run	fast	mug	cat	sink		

1. pot: _____ _____
2. strong: _____ _____
3. net: _____ _____
4. tent: _____ _____
5. bump: _____ _____
6. tug: _____ _____
7. wig: _____ _____
8. pin: _____ _____
9. that: _____ _____
10. mad: _____ _____
11. drink: _____ _____
12. band: _____ _____
13. fun: _____ _____
14. dust: _____ _____
15. mop: _____ _____
16. fist: _____ _____
17. pen: _____ _____
18. send: _____ _____
19. last: _____ _____

Find the word in the box that completes each sentence. Write the word on the line provided.

a	and	the	you	have	one	word	can	said	little

20. Julio _____ drive Cam to the bank.
21. She _____ she would return your pen.
22. Joseph has a gift for _____.
23. They _____ to leave work soon.
24. Only _____ more box will fit in the trunk.
25. My _____ sister is younger than I am.
26. I can't wait for _____ weekend.
27. Flynn has _____ new car.
28. Spencer can spell the _____.
29. Do you know Gina _____ Sonya?

Circle the word that best completes the sentence.

30. Did you _____ the stop sign?
    A. see   **B.** sea

31. The dog dug a _____ under the fence.
    A. whole   **B.** hole

32. She lived in New Jersey for _____ years.
    A. ate   **B.** eight

33. Felix and _____ will give the report.
    A. eye   **B.** I

34. Ellie read the _____ book in one night.
    A. whole   **B.** hole

35. We will take a trip to the _____
    A. see   **B.** sea

36. She _____ soup for lunch.
    A. ate   **B.** eight

37. Her right _____ is red.
    A. eye   **B.** I

Add the suffix to create a new word and write the word on the line provided. Then write a sentence with the new word.

38. letter + -s = _____

_____

39. car + -s = _____

_____

40. point + -ed = _____

_____

41. fix + -ed = _____

_____

42. meet + -ing = _____

_____

43. ring + -ing = _____

_____

LESSON 51: Writing Numbers

Numbers can be written in different ways. They can be written in **standard form** or **word form.**

In standard form, use digits (1, 2, 3…) for numbers.

In word form, use words (one, two, three…) for numbers.

Examples:

Standard form	24	678	1,359
Word form	twenty-four	six hundred seventy-eight	one thousand three hundred fifty-nine

Follow these rules when you write numbers.
- Use the word form when writing numbers one through ninety-nine except when writing a date or a money amount. Use the standard form when writing numbers 100 and over.
- Use the word form when a number starts a sentence.
- For numbers with two words, always use a hyphen between the words. This rule applies to numbers twenty-one to ninety-nine.
- In standard form, use a comma with numbers for one thousand and above. Put the first comma three spaces to the left. Place a comma every three digits.
    - 1,359
    - 21,359
    - 121,359
    - 1,121,359

PRACTICE

1. Complete the chart by writing the standard form or word form on the lines provided.

Numbers							
1	one	11	eleven	10	ten
2	_____	12	_____	20	_____
_____	three	13	thirteen	30	_____
4	four	_____	fourteen	_____	forty
5	_____	15	_____	50	fifty
6	six	_____	sixteen	60	_____
7	_____	17	_____	70	seventy
_____	eight	18	eighteen	80	_____
9	nine	19	nineteen	90	ninety

Write each number using the form in ( ).

2. 71

    _____
    (word form)

3. _____

    (standard form)

    sixty-four

4. _____

    (standard form)

    forty-one

5. 227

    _____
    (word form)

6. _____

    (standard form)

    one hundred sixty-two

7. 33

    _____
    (word form)

8. 528

    _____
    (word form)

9. _____

    (standard form)

    twelve

10. 51

    _____
    (word form)

11. _____

    (standard form)

    two thousand eight hundred sixty-five

Use the rules to choose the best number form for each sentence. Write the correct number form on the line.

12. 4   four   Dan started a new job on May _____, 2015.

13. 115   One hundred fifteen   _____ people attended the wedding.

14. 30   thirty   Only _____ percent of the workers will get a raise.

15. 9   nine   Lisa's daughter is _____ years old.

16. 123   one hundred twenty-three   The movers packed _____ boxes.

LESSON 52: Reading Clock Times

You can use numbers or words to write clock times.

Examples:

Numbers	12:00	3:30	8:43
Words	twelve o'clock	three thirty	eight forty-three

Follow these steps to read the time on a clock with hands.
- A clock has the numbers 1 to 12.
- Look at the hour hand. The hour hand is the shorter hand. It tells you the hour.
- Look at the minute hand. The minute hand is the longer hand. It tells you the minute. Each mark on the clock face stands for 1 minute. Each number stands for 5 minutes.

12 = :00	1 = :05	2 = :10	3 = :15	4 = :20	5 = :25
6 = :30	7 = :35	8 = :40	9 = :45	10 = :50	11 = :55

Example:

 The hour hand is on the six. The minute hand is on 12. The 12 stands for :00. The time shown on this clock would be written as 6:00 or six o'clock.

 The hour hand is just past the 2. The minute hand is on 7. The 7 stands for :35. The time on this clock would be written as 2:35 or two thirty-five.

PRACTICE

Use numbers to write the clock time. Write your answer on the line provided.

1.

_____

2.

_____

3.

_____

4.

_____

5.

_____

Use words to write the clock time. Write your answer on the line provided.

6.

_____

7.

_____

8.

_____

9.

_____

10.

_____

An hour can be divided into halves. A full hour is 60 minutes. A half hour is 30 minutes. When the minute hand of a clock is on 6, the time can be written as a **half past** an hour.

Example:

Half hour times can be written as 11:30, eleven thirty, or half past eleven.

An hour can also be divided into quarters. Quarter-hours are 15 minutes. When the minute hand is on 3, the time can be written as a **quarter past** an hour. When the minute hand is on 9, the time can be written as a **quarter to** an hour.

Examples:

The time on this clock could be written as 4:15, four fifteen, or a quarter past four.

The time on this clock could be written as 4:45, four forty-five, or a quarter to five. NOTE: When you use the phrase a quarter to, you count ahead to the next hour.

PRACTICE

Write the clock time using the phrase half past, a quarter past, **or** a quarter to. **Write your answer on the line provided.**

11.

_____

14.

_____

17.

_____

20.

_____

12.

_____

15.

_____

18.

_____

21.

_____

13.

_____

16.

_____

19.

_____

22.

_____

Fundamental Skills for Writing

LESSON 53: Writing Money Amounts

Money amounts can be written with numbers or with numbers and words. Follow these steps to write money amounts.

For more than one dollar
- Use the dollar sign ($) instead of the word *dollars*. Put the $ before the number.
- Use a decimal (.) instead of the word *and*.
- Put dollar amounts to the left of the decimal.
- Put cent amounts to the right of the decimal.
- If a number is one thousand or above, be sure to use a comma.

Examples:

The album cost **nine dollars and ninety-nine cents**. (word form)
The album costs **$9.99**. (standard form)

The computer cost **two thousand four hundred dollars and seventy-three cents**. (word form)
The computer cost **$2,400.73**. (standard form)

Do not use the dollar sign ($) and the word <u>dollars</u> together. Choose one.

Examples:

Her allowance is $5.
The lottery winner got $1 million.

Her allowance is 5 dollars.
The lottery winner got 1 million dollars.

For less than one dollar
- Use the word *cents* when writing an amount less than a dollar.
- Do not use a dollar sign ($).

Examples:

A stamp costs forty-nine cents. (word form)   A stamp costs 49 cents. (standard form)

Use the standard form and word form for money amounts on a check. Write the standard form in the box. Write the word form on the line. When writing the word form of a money amount, be sure to use a hyphen between the numbers twenty-one to ninety-nine.

Example:

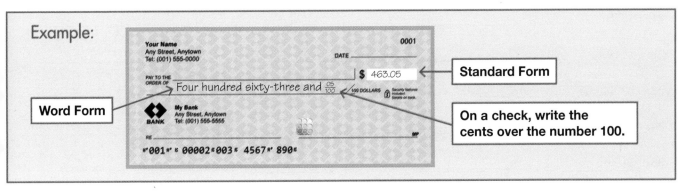

Write each money amount in standard form on the line provided.

1. Two dollars and thirty-nine cents $____.____ ____

2. One hundred thousand dollars $____ ____ ____ , ____ ____ ____

3. Nineteen dollars and fifty-five cents $____ ____ . ____ ____

4. Fifty-one dollars and three cents $____ ____ . ____ ____

5. Five million dollars $ ____ million

6. Twelve dollars and ten cents $____ ____ . ____ ____

7. Five hundred dollars $____ ____ ____

8. Twenty-four dollars and seventy-five cents $____ ____ . ____ ____

9. Seventeen cents   ____ ____ cents

10. Nine hundred eighty dollars and twenty-three cents $____ ____ ____ . ____ ____

Circle the money amount that is written correctly.

11.	$23.16	$23.16 cents	23.16
12.	$5346	$5346 dollars	$5,346
13.	$6	$6 dollars	6.00
14.	$72.16 dollars	72.16	$72.16
15.	167,891	$167891	$167,891
16.	.13	13 cents	.13 cents
17.	$one million	1 million dollars	$1 million dollars
18.	$23705.12	$23,705.12	$23705.12 dollars
19.	12.15 cents	$12.15 dollars	$12.15
20.	500.00	$500	$500 dollars

Write the word form for each money amount.

21. $575   _____

22. $119.47   _____

23. $2,340.05   _____

24. $32,500   _____

25. $15.60   _____

LESSON 54: Writing the Date

A **date** can be written in different ways. It can be written with words, numbers, or both.

Examples:

Words:	twenty-second day of January in the year two thousand sixteen
Words and Numbers:	January 22, 2016
Numbers:	01/22/2016
	01-22-2016

Writing a date with only words is very long. It is more common for people to use numbers and words or numbers only.

Words and Numbers

In the United States, dates are written in order by month, day, and year. Follow these steps to write a date with words and numbers.

- Spell out the name of the month.
- Write the number (1, 2, 3…) of the day. Use a comma after the day.
- Write the number of the year. Years do not have commas in them.

Examples:

April 3, 1998   June 13, 2017   December 24, 2030

Numbers

You can choose to use slashes or dashes to separate the numbers in a date. Follow these steps to write a date with numbers.

- Write the number of month. January is month 1. December is month 12.
  If the month is a single digit, put a zero in front. Use a slash or a dash after the month.
- Write the number of the day. If the day is a single digit, put a zero in front.
  Use a slash or a dash after the day.
- Write the number of the year.

Examples:

day/month/year	04/04/1998	06/13/2017	12/24/2030
day-month-year	04-04-1998	06-13-2017	12-24-2030

PRACTICE

1. Complete the chart. Write the word or number for each month on the line.

Name of Month	Number of Month
January	_____
February	_____
_____	3
April	_____
May	_____
_____	6
_____	7
August	_____
September	_____
_____	10
_____	11
December	_____

Use only numbers to write each date in the format shown in ( ). Write your answer on the line. The first one has been done for you.

Example: March 2, 2018 (dashes)   03-02-2018

2. October 23, 2016 (slashes)   _____

3. April 9, 2019 (slashes)   _____

4. September 28, 1982 (dashes)   _____

5. August 3, 2016 (dashes)   _____

Use numbers and words to write each date. Write your answer on the line. The first one has been done for you.

Example: 12/12/2020   December 12, 2020

6. 05-29-1956   _____

7. 03/07/2018   _____

8. 10-31-2019   _____

9. 04/16/1782   _____

Write the date. Use the two formats you have learned.

10. fifteenth day of February in the year two thousand twelve

    _____   _____

11. fifth day of June in the year two thousand eight

    _____   _____

12. thirtieth of July in the year two thousand thirty-two

    _____   _____

LESSON 55: Completing a Simple Form

During your life, you will complete forms in many different places. For example, you may complete a form from a doctor's office, a library, or a post office.

You will complete forms for different reasons. For example, you may use a form to order an item from a store. Or, you may use a form to complete your taxes.

Most forms ask for the same type of information. They ask for your name, address, and birthdate. They will ask for that information in different ways.

Follow these steps when completing a form.
- Look over the whole form first.
  Pay attention to special directions. For example, "use in blue or black ink" or "print only."
  Pay attention to parts that do not need to be filled out. They may be labeled "For office use only."
- Fill out parts of the form.
  Begin at the top left-hand corner.
  Complete the sections. Work from left to right and top to bottom.
  Check the back of the form. Fill out any sections on the back in the same order—left to right, top to bottom.
- If you cannot answer a section, do not skip it. Instead, write *N/A*. *N/A* stands for "not applicable" or "no answer." Writing *N/A* shows that you read the section but did not have an answer.
- When you finish filling in all the parts, read over the form one more time.
  Check the spelling of names and addresses.
  Check that numbers are correct.
  Make sure all sections that require an answer from you have an answer, even if it is N/A.
  Make sure you have signed and dated the form, if needed.

Example:

APPLICATION FOR LIBRARY CARD
Complete the form entirely. Please print. ← **Special Instructions**

David	R	Washington	06/30/1990
FIRST NAME	**MIDDLE**	**LAST NAME**	**DATE OF BIRTH**

555 That St.	Anycity	CO	12345
STREET ADDRESS	**CITY**	**STATE**	**ZIP**

→ N/A	555-555-5555	dr.washington@email.com
HOME PHONE	**CELL PHONE**	**EMAIL**

David R. Washington	05/22/2018
SIGNATURE	**DATE**

N/A here means he doesn't have a home phone.

PRACTICE

This form is an application for a grocery rewards card. Look over the form. Then, answer the questions.

MCCALL'S GROCERY REWARDS PROGRAM

APPLICANT

Last Name_____ First Name _____Middle Initial _____

Street Address _____ Apartment Number _____

City _____ State _____ Zip Code _____

Day Telephone Number (_____)_____

Evening Telephone Number (_____) _____

Applicant Signature _____ Date_____

FOR OFFICIAL USE ONLY: (Do not write below this line.)

Card Number _____ Approved By _____ Date _____

---

1. What would you write for Apartment Number if you don't live in an apartment?

   _____

2. Where should you sign your name?

   _____

3. What part of a telephone number goes in ( )?

   _____

4. Use the steps you have learned to complete the form. You can use your information. Or, you can make up information.

LESSON 56: Creating Tables and Charts

Tables

You use a table to organize data, or information. A **table** has rows and columns. Rows go from left to right. Columns go up and down. At the top of each column, there is a column head. The column head labels the information in that column.

Follow these steps to create a table.
- Read the data. Ask yourself, "What does the data have in common?" This will be the title of your table.
- Look for different types of data. These will be your column heads.
- Sort the data in the groups by type. Put the data in an order that makes sense. For example, you could put names in alphabetical order. You could put numbers in order from highest to lowest.

Example:

The company hired two new workers. Their names are Ronald Nolan and Cindy Martin. Cindy works in accounting. Ronald works in sales. Cindy's ID number is 24. Ronald's ID number is 82.

What does the data have in common? new employees
What categories are there? names, departments, ID number
How can you sort the details? arrange names in alphabetical order

Now review the table below. The data is easier to understand in this format.

New Employees		
Name	**Employee ID**	**Department**
Martin, Cindy	24	Accounting
Nolan, Ronald	82	Sales

PRACTICE

1. Read the information. Then add the data in the table. Some of the data has been placed in the table for you.

The E6 bus makes three trips each day. The bus begins at Main Street. Then, it goes to Western Avenue. Next, it arrives at 1st Street. Then, it goes back to Main Street.

The E6 arrives at Main Street at 5:40, 6:22, and 6:40. It arrives at Western Avenue at 5:55, 6:37, and 6:55. It arrives at 1st Street at 6:05, 6:47, and 7:05.

Trip	Arrive Main Street	_____	Arrive 1st Street
____			
2			6:47
____		6:55	

Charts

A chart uses symbols to show data. A **pie chart** is one type of chart. It uses slices to shows parts of a whole. It also shows how the different parts compare to one another.

Follow these steps to create a pie chart.
- Read the data. Ask yourself, "What does the data have in common?" This will be the title of your table.
- Look for different types of data. These will be the slices of the pie chart.
- Decide how large each slice of the data should be. The size will show how the part relates to the whole.
- Label each slice. Make sure all the slices add up to the total number.

Example:

> Our company has 70 workers. Twenty-nine work in IT. Twenty-five work in sales. Twelve work in the front office. Four work the warehouse.

What does the data have in common? number of workers
What does each slice stand for? IT, sales, front office, warehouse
How large should each slice be? IT = 29, sales = 25, front office = 12, warehouse = 4. IT is the largest slice. Warehouse is the smallest slice.

Here is the pie chart. The information is clear. You can see how the company is divided into departments. You can also see how the department sizes relate to one another.

Workers by Department

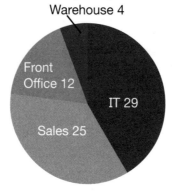

PRACTICE

2. Read the data. Add labels to the pie chart. The pie chart has been divided for you.

> The E6 bus makes three trips each day. On Friday, 100 people rode on the E6 bus. There were 52 people on Trip 1. There were 17 people on Trip 2. There were 31 people on Trip 3.

Riders on E6 Bus by Trip

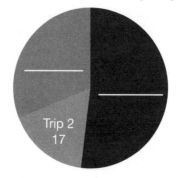

Fundamental Skills for Writing

Draw a line from each standard form number to its written form.

1. 58

2. 13

3. 5,694

4. 35

5. 2,100

A. two thousand one hundred

B five thousand six hundred ninety-four

C. thirty-five

D. thirteen

E. fifty-eight

Circle the choice that shows the correct clock time.

6.

7.

8.

9.

10.

6.
A. half past one
B. a quarter past one
C. 1:20
D. one o'clock

7.
A. a quarter past four
B. 4:40
C. four twenty-five
D. a quarter to five

8.
A. a quarter to two
B. a quarter past two
C. half past two
D. 2:06

9.
A. eight o'clock
B. 8:12
C. a quarter to eight
D. half past eight

10.
A. 9:03
B. half past nine
C. a quarter to nine
D. a quarter past nine

Circle the choice that shows the money amount written correctly.

11.
A. $769.54 dollars
B. 769.54
C. $769.54
D. $769.54 cents

12.
A. $five million
B. $5 million dollars
C. 5 million dollars
D. 5 million

13.
A. $435231
B. $435,231 dollars
C. 435231 dollars
D. $435,231

14.
A. 18 cents
B. 18
C. .18$
D. .18 cents

15.
A. $4 dollars
B. $4
C. 4.00
D. 4

16.
A. $4567
B. $4,567 dollars
C. 4,567 dollars
D. 4567 dollars

17. Complete the chart by writing a date in two different ways.

Words	Slashes	Dashes	Words and Numbers
sixth of April in the year two thousand eight	04/06/2008	_____	_____
_____	12/22/2016	12-22-2016	_____
fourteenth of October in the year two thousand eighteen	_____	_____	October 14, 2018
_____	06/10/2030	06-10-2030	_____
the twenty-fifth of November in the year two thousand ten	_____	_____	November 25, 2010

18. Complete the dog daycare application below. Base your answers on a real dog or a pretend one.

GOOD DOG DAYCARE APPLICATION FORM

Owner Information

Name: _____

Street Address: _____

City: _____ State: _____ Zip: _____

Home Phone: (_____) _____

Cell Phone: (_____) _____

Work Phone: (_____) _____

Pet Information

Name: _____ Sex: M/F   Age: _____

Breed: _____ Weight: _____ Color: _____

Owner Comments: _____

_____

_____

19. Read the information below. Add labels to the pie chart on the lines provided. The pie chart has been divided for you.

At Sam's Deli on Monday, 40 customers bought a salad for lunch, 21 bought a sandwich, 15 bought soup, 15 bought a drink, and 9 bought a dessert.

Monday Sales by Type

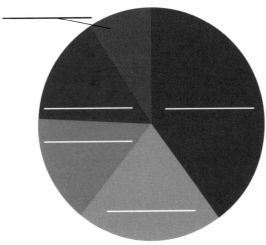

20. Read the information. Then add the data in the table. Some of the data has been placed in the table for you.

Each day, Sam receives boxes of apples, oranges, and bananas. On June 1, he received 125 apples, 74 oranges, and 97 bananas. On June 2, he received 118 apples, 84 oranges, and 100 bananas. On June 3, he received 164 apples, 72 oranges, and 88 bananas.

Date	_____	Oranges	Bananas
06/01	125	_____	97
_____	_____	84	_____
06/03	_____	_____	_____

Photo Credits

1 *apple* ©bergamont/Shutterstock; 1 *ball* ©Pavel Hlystov/Shutterstock; 1 *cup* ©Houghton Mifflin Harcourt; 2 *dog* ©Photodisc/Getty Images; 2 *egg* ©Comstock/Getty Images; 2 *fox* ©Eric Isselee/Shutterstock; 3 *gift* ©Steve Cole/Photodisc/Getty Images; 3 *horse* ©Getty Images; 3 *ink* ©Houghton Mifflin Harcourt; 4 *Jeep* ©Houghton Mifflin Harcourt; 4 *key* ©Getty Images; 4 *lion* ©Fotolia; 5 *money* ©Corbis; 5 *nest* ©richcano/iStockPhoto.com; 5 *ox* ©Eric Isselee/Shutterstock; 6 *piano* ©Getty Images; 6 *question* ©Getty Images; 6 *rake* ©Getty Images; 7 *sun* ©Getty Images; 7 *tiger* ©nattanan726/Shutterstock; 7 *umbrella* ©Comstock/Getty Images; 8 *vine* ©fuyu liu/Shutterstock; 8 *worm* ©Fstop/Getty Images; 8 *ax* ©Getty Images; 9 *yo-yo* ©Scott Rothstein/Shutterstock; 9 *zebra* ©Christian Musat/Shutterstock; 12 *ball* ©Pavel Hlystov/Shutterstock; 12 *bat* ©Kirsanov Valeriy Vladimirovich/Shutterstock; 12 *banana* ©Stockbyte/Getty Images; 12 *bus* ©Rob Wilson/Shutterstock; 12 *lamp* ©Getty Images; 12 *bench* ©DPD ImageStock/Alamy; 12 *desk* ©Houghton Mifflin Harcourt; 12 *web* ©Ulrike Henkys/Flickr/Getty Images; 12 *drum* ©Getty Images; 12 *cabin* ©Alamy; 12 *robin* ©Sebastian Knight/Shutterstock; 12 *mop* ©Houghton Mifflin Harcourt; 12 *window* ©WidStock/Alamy; 12 *butter* ©Datacraft Co Ltd/Getty Images; 12 *bee* ©Tomo Jesenicnik/Shutterstock; 13 *can* ©Houghton Mifflin Harcourt; 13 *carrot* ©Luis c Jiménez/Fotolia; 13 *tape* ©Christopher Elwell/Shutterstock; 13 *comb* ©Getty Images; 13 *cup* ©Houghton Mifflin Harcourt; 13 *cactus* ©Getty Images; 13 *mule* ©Photodisc/Getty Images; 13 *camel* ©Photodisc/Getty Images; 13 *cane* ©Burke/Triolo Productions/Getty Images; 13 *hat* ©Getty Images; 13 *volcano* ©iStockPhoto.com; 13 *camera* ©Houghton Mifflin Harcourt; 13 *shovel* ©Getty Images; 13 *dishes* ©B.A.E. Inc./Alamy Images; 13 *cot* ©Houghton Mifflin Harcourt; 14 *doll* ©Getty Images; 14 *door* ©Photocritical/Shutterstock; 14 *dime* ©Houghton Mifflin Harcourt; 14 *bell* ©Getty Images; 14 *dog* ©Photodisc/Getty Images; 14 *deer* ©Fotolia; 14 *dig* ©Houghton Mifflin Harcourt; 14 *spider* ©Getty Images; 14 *sheep* ©Getty Images; 14 *hand* ©Antonio Guillem/Shutterstock; 14 *bike* ©Comstock Images/Getty Images; 14 *candy* ©Sandra van der Steen/Shutterstock; 14 *water* ©Houghton Mifflin Harcourt; 15 *fish* ©Martin Harvey/Alamy; 15 *feather* ©Nguyen Thai/Shutterstock; 15 *fork* ©Getty Images; 15 *five* ©Getty Images; 15 *log* ©Getty Images; 15 *fence* ©Zelfit/Shutterstock; 15 *fox* ©Eric Isselee/Shutterstock; 15 *girl* ©Shutterstock; 15 *roof* ©Timothy Large/Alamy; 15 *book* ©Getty Images; 15 *elf* ©azndc/iStockPhoto.com; 15 *ruler* ©joebelanger/iStockPhoto.com; 15 *fan* ©Alamy; 16 *gum* ©Getty Images; 16 *bunny* ©Halina Yakushevich/Shutterstock; 16 *guitar* ©Yevgen Timashov/Alamy; 16 *duck* ©Mircea Bezergheanu/Shutterstock; 16 *goat* ©Eric Isselee/Shutterstock; 16 *gift* ©Steve Cole/Photodisc/Getty Images; 16 *tub* ©Houghton Mifflin Harcourt; 16 *golf* ©Blue Jean Images/Corbis; 16 *game* ©Alamy; 16 *wagon* ©Hank Shiffman/Shutterstock; 16 *lock* ©Photodisc/C Squared Studios/Getty Images; 16 *pig* ©Eric Isselee/Shutterstock; 16 *fork* ©Getty Images; 16 *robe* ©Getty Images; 16 *bug* ©Vinicius Tupinamba/Shutterstock; 17 *hand* ©Antonio Guillem/Shutterstock; 17 *ant* ©iStockPhoto.com; 17 *hat* ©Getty Images; 17 *table* ©Houghton Mifflin Harcourt; 17 *horse* ©Getty Images; 17 *house* ©Getty Images; 17 *hammer* ©Comstock/Getty Images; 17 *ice* ©Zoom Team/Shutterstock; 17 *hen* ©s_oleg/Shutterstock; 17 *hay* ©Alamy; 17 *nail* ©Houghton Mifflin Harcourt; 17 *hook* ©Brian Hagiwara/Getty Images; 17 *hose* ©DElight/iStockPhoto.com; 17 *top* ©Corbis; 17 *heart* ©Alamy; 18 *jar* ©iStockPhoto.com; 18 *judge* ©Getty Images; 18 *jeans* ©C. Squared Studios/Photodisc/Getty Images; 18 *jacket* ©Houghton Mifflin Harcourt; 18 *ham* ©Getty Images; 18 *Jeep* ©Houghton Mifflin Harcourt; 18 *map* ©Getty Images; 18 *jack* ©Getty Images; 18 *bee* ©Tomo Jesenicnik/Shutterstock; 18 *jump* ©Shutterstock; 18 *jewelry* ©Getty Images; 18 *rope* ©Getty Images; 18 *tools* ©Brand X Pictures/Getty Images; 19 *king* ©Joshua Ets-Hokin/Photodisc/Getty Images; 19 *kangaroo* ©Louise Heusinkveld/Alamy; 19 *key* ©Getty Images; 19 *lamb* ©Getty Images; 19 *kite* ©Houghton Mifflin Harcourt; 19 *kitten* ©Siede Preis/Getty Images; 19 *door* ©Photocritical/Shutterstock; 19 *kick* ©Getty Images; 19 *turkey* ©Alamy; 19 *book* ©Houghton Mifflin Harcourt; 19 *rug* ©Sdbphoto carpets/Alamy; 19 *tape* ©Christopher Elwell/Shutterstock; 19 *skunk* ©Photodisc/Getty Images; 20 *leaf* ©Getty Images; 20 *lion* ©Fotolia; 20 *soap* ©Tina Rencelj/Shutterstock; 20 *ladder* ©C Squared Studios/Photodisc/Getty Images; 20 *log* ©Getty Images; 20 *lemon* ©Comstock/Getty Images; 20 *nose* ©Houghton Mifflin Harcourt; 20 *lizard* ©werg/Shutterstock; 20 *camel* ©Photodisc/Getty Images; 20 *owl* ©Getty Images; 20 *frame* ©Shutterstock; 20 *lock* ©Photodisc/C Squared Studios/Getty Images; 20 *team* ©Houghton Mifflin Harcourt; 20 *fire* ©seeyou/Shutterstock; 20 *lake* ©Ryan DeBerardinis/Shutterstock; 21 *moon* ©Stocktrek Images, Inc./Photodisc/Getty Images; 21 *mouse* ©Eric Isselee/Shutterstock; 21 *mitten* ©Houghton Mifflin Harcourt; 21 *newspaper* ©Houghton Mifflin Harcourt; 21 *man* ©Getty Images; 21 *rainbow* ©Corbis; 21 *map* ©Getty Images; 21 *milk* ©Photodisc/Getty Images; 21 *drum* ©Getty Images; 21 *ten* ©Houghton Mifflin Harcourt; 21 *sink* ©C Squared Studios/Getty Images; 21 *money* ©Corbis; 21 *cone* ©Alamy; 21 *gum* ©Getty Images; 21 *woman* ©Getty Images; 22 *nose* ©Houghton Mifflin Harcourt; 22 *nine* ©Houghton Mifflin Harcourt; 22 *mop* ©Houghton Mifflin Harcourt; 22 *nail* ©Houghton Mifflin Harcourt; 22 *nest* ©richcano/iStockPhoto.com; 22 *nickel* ©Houghton Mifflin Harcourt; 22 *yard* ©Iriana Shiyan/Shutterstock; 22 *nurse* ©Getty Images; 22 *sun* ©Getty Images; 22 *mail* ©Alamy; 22 *window* ©WidStock/Alamy; 22 *jet* ©Stocktrek Images, Inc./Digital Vision/Getty Images; 22 *needle* ©Houghton Mifflin Harcourt; 23 *pig* ©Eric Isselee/Shutterstock; 23 *goat* ©Eric Isselee/Shutterstock; 23 *pineapple* ©Houghton Mifflin Harcourt; 23 *piano* ©Getty Images; 23 *pencil* ©Houghton Mifflin Harcourt; 23 *pears* ©Getty Images; 23 *ship* ©Corbis; 23 *robin* ©Sebastian Knight/Shutterstock; 23 *bell* ©Getty Images; 23 *purse* ©Getty Images; 23 *football* ©Corbis; 23 *sheep* ©Getty Images; 23 *pillow* ©Brand X Pictures/Getty Images; 24 *quail* ©J.S. Fisher/Shutterstock;

50 *mule* ©Photodisc/Getty Images; 50 *cube* ©leminuit/iStockPhoto.com; 50 *duck* ©Mircea Bezergheanu/Shutterstock; 50 *dune* ©Moodboard/Corbis; 50 *juice* ©Mark Herreid/Shutterstock; 50 *tune* ©Superstock; 50 *ten* ©Houghton Mifflin Harcourt; 50 *tube* ©Houghton Mifflin Harcourt; 50 *unicycle* ©iStockPhoto.com; 50 *glue* ©Alamy; 50 *watch* ©Alamy; 50 *flute* ©Getty Images; 50 *chick* ©Getty Images; 50 *ruler* ©joebelanger/iStockPhoto.com; 50 *glove* ©Enigma/Alamy; 51 *bread* ©maxim ibragimov/Shutterstock; 51 *scale* ©Corbis; 51 *rein* ©Getty Images; 51 *head* ©Belinka/Shutterstock; 51 *veil* ©Getty Images; 51 *sweater* ©Houghton Mifflin Harcourt; 51 *pear* ©Getty Images; 51 *weight* ©Getty Images; 51 *tread* ©Vincenzo Lombardo/Getty Images; 51 *neighbors* ©Houghton Mifflin Harcourt; 51 *feather* ©iStockPhoto.com; 51 *eight* ©Getty Images; 51 *yarn* ©Shutterstock; 51 *spread* ©Houghton Mifflin Harcourt; 51 *sleigh* ©Getty Images; 51 *treasure* ©Comstock/Getty Images; 51 *veins* ©Houghton Mifflin Harcourt; 51 *weather* ©Houghton Mifflin Harcourt; 52 *book* ©Getty Images; 52 *moon* ©Stocktrek Images, Inc./Photodisc/Getty Images; 52 *wood* ©Ales Veluscek/iStockPhoto.com; 52 *roof* ©Timothy Large/Alamy; 52 *hoop* ©Corbis; 52 *wool* ©Echo/Getty Images; 52 *raccoon* ©Getty Images; 52 *school* ©Shutterstock; 52 *zoo* ©Houghton Mifflin Harcourt; 52 *pool* ©Shutterstock; 52 *kangaroo* ©Louise Heusinkveld/Alamy; 52 *balloon* ©pixelman/Shutterstock; 52 *boot* ©Getty Images; 52 *spoon* ©Getty Images; 53 *screw* ©Photodisc/Getty Images; 53 *fruit* ©iStockPhoto.com; 53 *jewel* ©Rozaliya/Shutterstock; 53 *suit* ©Shutterstock; 53 *newspaper* ©Getty Images; 53 *stew* ©Getty Images; 53 *chew* ©Lightly Salted/Alamy; 53 *juice* ©Mark Herreid/Shutterstock; 54 *haul* ©Comstock/Getty Images; 54 *kitten* ©Africa Studio/Shutterstock; 54 *chalk* ©Getty Images; 54 *ball* ©Pavel Hlystov/Shutterstock; 54 *fall* ©Labrynthe/Shutterstock; 54 *yawn* ©Shutterstock; 54 *walk* ©Shutterstock; 54 *vault* ©Corbis; 54 *saw* ©Getty Images; 54 *faucet* ©Getty Images; 54 *lawn* ©06photo/Shutterstock; 54 *wall* ©Houghton Mifflin Harcourt; 54 *saucer* ©Getty Images; 54 *crawl* ©Houghton Mifflin Harcourt; 54 *astronaut* ©Getty Images; 54 *hawk* ©Getty Images; 54 *sun* ©Flash-ka/Shutterstock; 54 *shawl* ©Alamy; 54 *salt* ©Getty Images; 54 *Autumn* ©Echo/Getty Images; 55 *mouse* ©Eric Isselee/Shutterstock; 55 *couch* ©BimpaStudio/Shutterstock; 55 *house* ©Getty Images; 55 *mountain* ©Getty Images; 55 *door* ©Photocritical/Shutterstock; 55 *cougar* ©Fotolia; 55 *flour* ©Shutterstock; 55 *mouth* ©Getty Images; 55 *toad* ©Tom Reichner/Shutterstock; 55 *food* ©Houghton Mifflin Harcourt; 55 *spout* ©Alamy; 55 *gourd* ©Getty Images; 55 *blouse* ©Africa Studio/Shutterstock; 55 *four* ©Getty Images; 55 *yawn* ©Shutterstock; 55 *rough* ©Ron Chapple Stock/Alamy; 55 *cloud* ©Shutterstock; 56 *cow* ©Henk Bentlage/Shutterstock; 56 *crow* ©Life on White/Alamy; 56 *boy* ©Getty Images; 56 *oil* ©Getty Images; 56 *point* ©Shutterstock; 56 *toys* ©Getty Images; 56 *soil* ©LJSPhotography/Alamy; 56 *coil* ©Corbis; 56 *noise* ©Getty Images; 56 *broil* ©Getty Images; 56 *oyster* ©Getty Images; 56 *boil* ©iStockPhoto.com; 56 *foil* ©Mike Lawrence/iStockPhoto.com; 56 *flower* ©Getty Images; 56 *crown* ©nicoolay/iStockPhoto.com; 56 *snow* ©Kotenko Oleksandr/Shutterstock; 56 *owl* ©Brian Hagiwara/Brand X Pictures/Getty Images; 56 *clown* ©Getty Images; 56 *coins* ©Asaf Eliason/Shutterstock; 57 *car* ©Robert Churchill/Getty Images; 57 *corn* ©iStockPhoto.com; 57 *church* ©Alamy; 57 *bird* ©Steve Byland/Shutterstock; 57 *herd* ©Alamy; 57 *barn* ©Scott Prokop/Shutterstock; 57 *banana* ©Stockbyte/Getty Images; 57 *jar* ©iStockPhoto.com; 57 *shark* ©Nantawat Chotsuwan/Shutterstock; 57 *man* ©Getty Images; 57 *harp* ©Getty Images; 57 *stork* ©Niels Poulsen/Alamy; 57 *fork* ©Getty Images; 57 *cot* ©Houghton Mifflin Harcourt; 57 *horse* ©Getty Images; 57 *bench* ©DPD ImageStock/Alamy; 57 *thorn* ©2009 HMH Guy Jarvis Photographer; 57 *skirt* ©Alexander Kalina/Shutterstock; 57 *hammer* ©Comstock/Getty Images; 57 *nurse* ©Getty Images; 57 *girl* ©Shutterstock; 57 *stir* ©Joseph C. Salonis/Shutterstock; 57 *surf* ©Real Deal Photo/Shutterstock; 57 *purse* ©Getty Images; 57 *fern* ©Leaves galore/Den Reader/Alamy; 58 *pig* ©Eric Isselee/Shutterstock; 58 *cat* ©Greenfire/Shutterstock; 58 *sun* ©Flash-ka/Shutterstock; 58 *bed* ©Comstock Images/Getty Images; 58 *lock* ©Photodisc/C Squared Studios/Getty Images; 58 *gum* ©Getty Images; 58 *bib* ©Houghton Mifflin Harcourt; 58 *hat* ©Getty Images; 58 *vest* ©Houghton Mifflin Harcourt; 58 *mop* ©Houghton Mifflin Harcourt; 58 *lamp* ©Getty Images; 58 *fish* ©Martin Harvey/Alamy; 59 *mule* ©Photodisc/Getty Images; 59 *hay* ©Alamy; 59 *hose* ©DElight/iStockPhoto.com; 59 *sail* ©Niels-DK/Alamy; 59 *leaf* ©Getty Images; 59 *kite* ©Andrey Parfenov/iStockPhoto.com; 59 *eagle* ©Getty Images; 59 *toad* ©Tom Reichner/Shutterstock; 59 *feet* ©Oleksii Sagitov/Shutterstock; 59 *cane* ©Burke/Triolo Productions/Getty Images; 59 *bone* ©Getty Images; 59 *play* ©Alamy; 60 *wall* ©Houghton Mifflin Harcourt; 60 *arrow* ©Houghton Mifflin Harcourt; 60 *suit* ©Shutterstock; 60 *surf* ©Real Deal Photo/Shutterstock; 60 *fork* ©Getty Images; 60 *girl* ©Shutterstock; 60 *barn* ©Scott Prokop/Shutterstock; 60 *car* ©Robert Churchill/Getty Images; 60 *fern* ©Leaves galore/Den Reader/Alamy; 60 *box* ©Daniel Fung/Shutterstock; 60 *bike* ©Comstock Images/Getty Images; 60 *juice* ©Mark Herreid/Shutterstock; 60 *shark* ©Nantawat Chotsuwan/Shutterstock; 60 *crawl* ©Houghton Mifflin Harcourt; 60 *goat* ©Eric Isselee/Shutterstock; 60 *stork* ©Niels Poulsen/Alamy; 60 *rope* ©Getty Images; 60 *cake* ©Jiri Vaclavek/Shutterstock; 60 *duck* ©Mircea Bezergheanu/Shutterstock; 60 *boy* ©Getty Images; 60 *stir* ©Joseph C. Salonis/Shutterstock; 61 *dad* ©Getty Images; 61 *sad* ©Shutterstock; 61 *band* ©Blend Images/Alamy; 61 *hand* ©Antonio Guillem/Shutterstock; 61 *fast* ©Mark Evans/iStockPhoto.com; 61 *mast* ©Houghton Mifflin Harcourt; 61 *cat* ©Greenfire/Shutterstock; 61 *rat* ©GK Hart/Vikki Hart/Photodisc/Getty Images; 62 *hat* ©Getty Images; 62 *pad* ©Getty Images; 62 *sand* ©Getty Images; 62 *track* ©Alamy; 62 *cast* ©Getty Images; 62 *land* ©gkuna/Shutterstock; 62 *doormat* ©Getty Images; 62 *mad* ©Getty Images; 63 *jet* ©Stocktrek Images, Inc./Digital Vision/Getty Images; 63 *set* ©Flashover/Alamy; 63 *hen* ©s_oleg/Shutterstock; 63 *ten* ©Houghton Mifflin Harcourt; 63 *tent* ©Getty Images; 63 *penny* ©Houghton Mifflin Harcourt; 63 *bend* ©Getty Images; 63 *mail* ©Getty Images; 64 *net* ©STILLFX/Shutterstock; 64 *men* ©Getty Images; 64 *blend* ©Houghton Mifflin Harcourt; 64 *dent* ©Alamy;

NOTES

NOTES

NOTES

NOTES